Success
10 Minute Tests

Maths
age 10 –11 · levels 4 – 5

Jason White

Sample page

clear instructional text

topic being covered

test number for quick reference

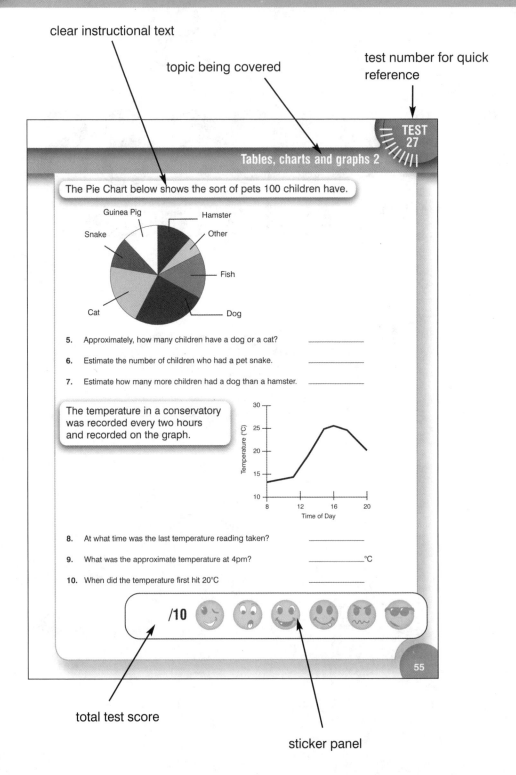

TEST
27

Tables, charts and graphs 2

The Pie Chart below shows the sort of pets 100 children have.

Guinea Pig   Hamster

Snake   Other

Fish

Cat   Dog

5.   Approximately, how many children have a dog or a cat?   _____

6.   Estimate the number of children who had a pet snake.   _____

7.   Estimate how many more children had a dog than a hamster.   _____

The temperature in a conservatory was recorded every two hours and recorded on the graph.

Temperature (°C)

30
25
20
15
10
      8   12   16   20
        Time of Day

8.   At what time was the last temperature reading taken?   _____

9.   What was the approximate temperature at 4pm?   _____°C

10. When did the temperature first hit 20°C   _____

/10

55

total test score

sticker panel

2

Contents

1. Put a circle around the largest number below.

   10,358   10,538   10,835   10,700   10,799

2. Write the value of the digit in bold in each number.

   a)   1,289   _____   **b)**   12,289   _____

   c)   128,952   _____

3. Calculate the following.

   a)   1327 + 72 + 154 =   _____

   b)   549 + 91 + 3584 =   _____

   c)   2057 + 1424 + 49 =   _____

4. Put these numbers in order, starting with the **smallest.**

   a)   2,851   1,067   2,809   2,799   4,001

   b)   6,430   6,515   7,000   6,001   6,099

5. Put these numbers in order, starting with the **largest.**

   a)   10,380   10,019   9,984   11,111   10,307

   b)   40,440   40,019   49,984   5,987   40,621

6. Order these decimals, starting with the **smallest.**

   a)   4.2   4.03   4.27   4.09   4.099

   b)   20.9   20.72   24.27   20.01   24.4

7. Order these fractions, starting with the **largest.**

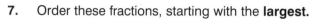

$\dfrac{1}{2}$ $\dfrac{1}{4}$ $\dfrac{1}{10}$ $\dfrac{1}{8}$ $\dfrac{3}{8}$

8. Six boys from class 4 have their height measured.

| Jon | Eric | Ahmed | Jake | George | Billy |
| 1.38m | 1.19m | 1.4m | 1.09m | 1.2m | 1.41m |

a) Who is the tallest boy? _____

b) Who is the second smallest boy? _____

c) Who is the third tallest boy? _____

9. The cost of five train journeys are as follows:

A   Nottingham – Lincoln   £8   **B**   Macclesfield – Stoke   £6.50

C   Carlisle – Manchester   £11.29   **D**   London – Bristol   £22

E   Brighton – London   £14.90

a) Write the letter of the cheapest journey. _____

b) Write the letter of the 2nd least expensive journey. _____

c) Write the letter of the most expensive journey. _____

10. The number of points a football team earned during a season is shown in the table below.

Team Name	Points
United	58
Rovers	74
City	64
Athletic	90
Albion	32

a) Which team earned the 2nd least amount of points?

_____

b) Which team earned the 3rd most points?

_____

/10

1. Round these numbers to the **nearest 10.**

   a)   435   367   901   251   665

   b)   6,478   7,045   8,889   5,807   1,555

   c)   29,837   17,995   21,001   99,507   56,219

2. Round these numbers to the **nearest 100.**

   a)   239   965   687   309   498

   b)   5,809   4,150   6,668   3,359   7,619

   c)   23,059   57,868   30,951   89,982   46,527

   d)   128,308   451,222   927,010   369,971   700,960

3. Round these numbers to the **nearest 1000.**

   a)   560   2,506   6,444   8,099   4,219

   b)   11,555   29,537   68,299   37,085   99,608

   c)   222,481   708,564   501,901   199,489   449,738

4. Here are the heights of 6 children.

Child 1	Child 2	Child 3	Child 4	Child 5	Child 6
1.24m	1.31m	1.2m	1.41m	1.33m	1.49m

Round each child's height to the nearest 10cm.

Child 1 = _____   Child 2 = _____   Child 3 = _____

Child 4 = _____   Child 5 = _____   Child 6 = _____

5. Estimate the answers to the questions below and then check your answers with a calculator.

Question	Estimate	Answer
2,129 + 3,454		
24,783 + 15,031		
7.92 + 15.01		
5,203 − 3,487		

6. Estimate how much water is in this jug.

_____ ml

7. Look at these scales and estimate the weight.

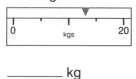

_____ kg

8. The boy below is 123cm tall. Estimate the height of the woman standing next to him.

_____ cm

9. Lily can read 2 pages in her reading book in 4 minutes and 6 seconds. Approximately how long will it take Lily to read 30 pages?

_____ minutes _____ seconds

10. Approximately, how many weeks are there in 50 years?

_____ weeks

/10

1. Work out the next two numbers in this sequence.

3	6	12	24		

2. Work out the next two numbers in this sequence.

160	80	40	20		

3. Draw the next two shapes in this sequence.

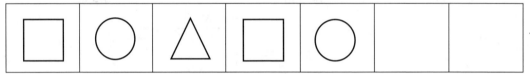

4. Work out the missing number in this sequence.

−14	−8		4	10	16

5. Work out the missing numbers in this sequence.

13	5		−11	−19	

6. The temperature in a fridge is −4°C. When the electricity is turned off, the temperature rises by 3°C every hour. What is the temperature in the fridge 4 hours after the electricity is turned off?

_____°C

7. A liquid freezes at -16C. Some of the frozen liquid is heated up by 6°C every 30 minutes. What is the temperature of the liquid after 2 hours of heating?

_____°C

Number patterns and negative numbers

8. Look at the thermometer.

   If the temperature cooled by 18°C, what would be the new reading on the thermometer?

   _____°C

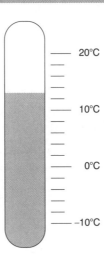

9. Look at the thermometer.

   If the temperature heated up by 14°C, what would be the new reading on the thermometer?

   _____°C

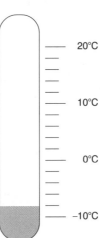

10. A thermometer reads 27°C. If the temperature drops by 3°C every 2 hours, how long would it take for the temperature to reach −9°C?

    _____ hours

/10

1. Work out the value of q in the following equation.

   $215 - q = 148$ _____

2. What is the value of z in the equation below?

   $z + 92 = 308$ _____

3. $s + t + w = 112$, if $s = 32$ and $t = w$, what is the value of w?

   _____

4. There are 146 marbles in a jar. 18 are red, 28 are green and the rest are blue or yellow. There are 3 times more yellow than blue. Work out:

   Blue marbles = _____   Yellow marbles = _____

5. In a cinema there were 200 adults and children. If there was one adult for every three children, how any adults and children were there?

   Adults = _____

   Children = _____

6. Look at the following equation.

$z + 31 = 58$

What is the value of z?

$z = $ _____

7. A rectangle has a perimeter of 54cm. The length of the longest sides are double that of the shortest sides. What are the lengths of the sides?

Shortest = _____

Longest = _____

8. A boy is 8 years older than his sister. How old is his sister when he is three times older than her?

_____

9. $a = 9, b = 2a, c = b - a$

What is the value of c if a is doubled? $c = $ _____

10. $66z = 11y$. If $z = 7$:

What is the value of y? $y = $ _____

/10

Fractions

1. Put the following fractions in the correct place in the sorting diagram below:

$$\frac{1}{2} \qquad \frac{11}{8} \qquad \frac{8}{10} \qquad 6\frac{1}{3} \qquad \frac{6}{4} \qquad 3\frac{7}{12}$$

Proper Fraction	Improper Fraction	Mixed Number Fraction

2. Look at the shapes below. What fraction of the shapes are shaded?

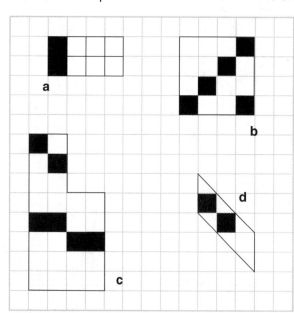

a = _____

b = _____

c = _____

d = _____

3. Write a fraction that is equivalent to each of the following decimals.

a 0.75 _____   b 2.4 _____   c 0.01 _____

d 8.125 _____   e 0.17 _____   f 0.875 _____

Fractions

4. Put the following fractions in the correct order from smallest to largest.

$$\frac{2}{5} \qquad \frac{6}{4} \qquad \frac{1}{3} \qquad \frac{8}{10} \qquad \frac{7}{15} \qquad \frac{1}{2}$$

    _____ _____ _____ _____ _____ _____

5. Calculate $\frac{3}{7}$ of £56.   £ _____

6. What is $\frac{3}{4}$ of 4.4 litres?   _____ l

5. Jim is given a $\frac{2}{7}$ share of some money. The amount he gets is £3.80.

    How much money was there before Jim got his share? £ _____

8. There are 92 chocolates in a tin. $\frac{1}{4}$ are soft centred, the rest are hard centred.

    How many are hard centred? _____

9. A fully loaded car weighs 1430kg. The passengers weigh $\frac{2}{5}$ of the total weight.

    How much does the car weigh without the passengers inside? _____ kg

10. Look at the jug of water below.

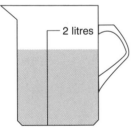

    2 litres

    The jug is $\frac{4}{5}$ full. How much water is in the jug?

    _____ ml

/10

Decimals

1. Put a circle around the largest decimal below.

   8.02   8.002   8.2   8.022   8.020

2. Write the value of the digit in bold in each number.

   a)   14.**0**5   _____

   b)   14.**5**   _____

   c)   14.00**5**   _____

3. Double the following decimals.

   a)   0.3   _____

   b)   1.4   _____

   c)   3.82   _____

   d)   0.09   _____

4. Work out the answers to these calculations.

   a)   1.2 x 3 =   _____

   b)   4.08 x 5 =   _____

   c)   6.1 x 7 =   _____

   d)   13.02 x 2 =   _____

5. Work out the answers to these calculations.

   a)   3.8 − 2.2 =   _____

   b)   4.9 + 6.3 =   _____

   c)   18.09 − 4.2 =   _____

   d)   23.6 + 14.23 =   _____

6. Harry has a weekly shopping list. This week he decides to get two weeks worth of shopping in one go. Write the new amounts Harry must get.

	old amount	new amount
Carrots	1200g	kg
Potatoes	2.5kg	kg
Tomatoes	0.45kg	kg
Onions	3	
Peas	300g	kg

7. Class 3 did a sponsored walk. They split into six groups and the money they raised was as follows:

Group 1 = £13.28   Group 2 = £10.50   Group 3 = 1571p

Group 4 = £8   Group 5 = 1108p   Group 6 = £12.99

How much money did class 3 raise altogether?   £ _____

8. Here are the weights of some children. Work out how much they weigh altogether.

25.4kg, 28.72kg, 21.8kg, 30.02kg, 33.19kg, 24.5kg   _____ kg

9. A jug can hold 2200ml of water. It takes 100 jugs of water to fill a tank. How much water can the tank hold if it is full? Give your answer in litres. _____ l

10. Mary measures her stride. It is 85cm. If Mary takes 200 strides, how many metres has she gone? _____ m

/10

Addition

1. Calculate the answer to the following additions.

   a) Thirteen add fifty eight. _____

   b) Seventy five add thirty four. _____

   c) Forty six add ninety seven. _____

2. Add these numbers.

   a) 128 + 308 _____

   b) 437 + 292 _____

   c) 830 + 405 _____

3. Now work these out.

   a)   45   b)   83   c)   72
       +61   +39   +29
       ____   ____   ____

4. Calculate the additions below.

   a)   138   b)   528   c)   631
       +457   +604   +729
       ____   ____   ____

5. Add together 583, 692, 571, 904 and 300.

   _____

6. Bill goes to the cinema and spends £4.60 to watch the film. He also buys popcorn which costs £2.75 a bag. How much does Bill spend altogether?

   £ _____

7. Jenny goes shopping and buys a dress, a top and a pair of shoes.
   Calculate how much money Jenny spends.

Dress	£14.90
Top	£9.99
Shoes	£54.50

   £ _____

8. How many metres of painting do they need to mark out all of the lines on this netball court?

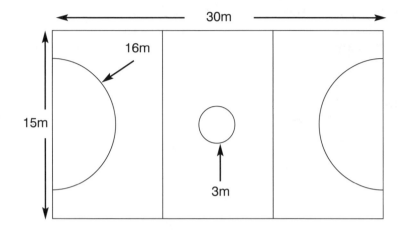

_____ m

9. How much money do these three children have altogether?

£ _____

£8.43   £3.82

£4.77

10. Write in the missing digits.

| 8 | | 9 | **+** | | 6 | 4 | **=** | 9 | 9 | 3 |

/10

1. Calculate the answer to the following subtractions.

   a) Seventy three subtract twenty seven. _____

   b) Ninety four subtract thirty six. _____

   c) Fifty one subtract eighteen. _____

2. Subtract these numbers.

   a) 571 – 358 _____

   b) 907 – 668 _____

   c) 325 – 179 _____

3. Calculate the subtractions below.

   a)   82   b)   53   c)   61
       −34   −37   −19
       ____   ____   ____

4. Find the answers to these subtractions.

   a)   742   b)   259   c) 1058
       −178   −83   −591
       ____   ____   ____

5. Take away 265,096 from 1,062,884.

   _____

6. Heather has £20. She spends £12.27 in the shop. How much money does she have left?

   £ _____

7. Emily went shopping and spent £8.90 on food, £2.50 on some socks and £15 on a dress. How much money did she have left out of £30?

   £ _____

8. The baker had 6kg of flour. He needed 225g of flour to make each cake. If he makes 12 cakes, how much flour does he have left?

   _____ kg

9. A full tank holds 520 litres of water. The tank is then drained by pulling the plug out. 40 litres of water is drained through the plug hole every minute. How many minutes will it take until the tank holds 200 litres?

   _____ mins

10. Write in the missing digits.

   | 9 | 4 | | — | 3 | 9 | 8 | = | | 4 | 6 |

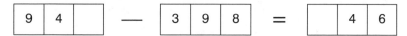

/10

1. Write down the multiples of the following pairs of numbers.

    a)   6 and 2   _____

    b)   7 and 9   _____

    c)   20 and 2   _____

2. Circle all the multiples of 6.

    18   66   16   96   46

3. Circle all the multiples of 9.

    19   29   27   180   35

4. Calculate the answers to these multiplications.

    a)   12 x 7 = _____   **b)**   20 x 3 = _____

    c)   6 x 15 = _____   **d)**   9 x 18 = _____

5. Calculate 24 x 37.

    _____

6. Calculate 46 x 17.

    _____

7. There were 87 people watching a film at the cinema. They paid £4 each to get in.
How much did the cinema take?

£ _____

8. A music concert has 54 rows of seats. There are 28 seats in each row.
How many people can have seats during the concert?

_____

9. A box of marbles has 35 marbles in it. There are 24 boxes in the shop.
How many marbles are there altogether?

_____

10. Class 7 went on a day trip by train to the seaside.
37 children and 5 adults went on the trip.
How much did the trip cost?

£ _____

Train trip to the Seaside	
Adults (return)	£12.50
Children (return)	£6.75

/10

1. Write down all the factors of these numbers.

   a) 24 _____

   b) 35 _____

   c) 42 _____

2. Circle all the numbers which have a factor of 8.

   60   80   18   24   64

3. Circle all the numbers which have a factor of 3.

   72   30   13   29   18

4. Calculate the answers to these divisions.

   a) $84 \div 4 =$ _____

   b) $72 \div 9 =$ _____

   c) $120 \div 5 =$ _____

   d) $22 \div 7 =$ _____

5. Calculate $248 \div 7$.

   _____

6. Calculate $671 \div 9$.

   _____

7. Olivia has 97 sweets in a jar. She shares the sweets fairly between herself and 3 friends. How many sweets does each child have? How many are left over?

_____ sweets each

_____ sweets left over

8. There are 472 children at a football tournament. Teams are made up of eight players. How many teams are there altogether?

_____ teams

9. Fred has ten 2 litre bottles of pop for his party. A cup of pop is 300ml. How many cups of pop will Fred have?

_____ cups

10. Kate has £200 to spend on her birthday party. Party bags cost £5 each and food is £2 each. How many children including herself can go to the party and have both food and a party bag?

_____ children

/10

1. Write the following fractions as a percentage.

   a) $\frac{1}{2}$ _____

   b) $\frac{1}{4}$ _____

   c) $\frac{3}{10}$ _____

   d) $\frac{3}{4}$ _____

2. Write the following decimals as percentages.

   a) 0.34 _____

   b) 0.57 _____

   c) 0.7 _____

   d) 0.03 _____

3. Write the following percentages as decimals.

   a) 49% _____

   b) 72% _____

   c) 5% _____

   d) 60% _____

4. What percentages of the grids below are shaded?

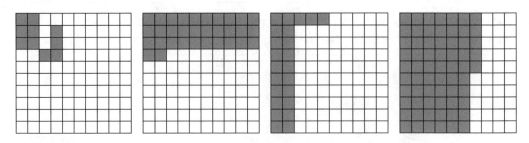

a _____%   b _____%   c _____%   d _____%

5. Calculate 50% of the following amounts.

    a) 42kg   _____ kg

    b) 64l   _____ l

    c) 3km   _____ km

    d) £70   £ _____

6. Calculate 30% of the following amounts.

    a) £120   £ _____

    b) 200m   _____ m

    c) £4.00   £ _____

    d) 600kg   _____ kg

7. There is a sale in a local game store. The sign says 25% off.
Tim buys a game that originally cost £24. How much change does Tim get from £20?

£ _____

8. Sarah puts £300 in a bank account. The money earns 7% interest per year.
How much money does Sarah have in the account after 1 years' interest is added?

£ _____

9. A man who weighs 92kg decides to go on a diet. He loses 10% of his weight.
What is his new weight?

_____ kg

10. A road is 800km long. The length is increased by 25%. How long is the road now?

_____ km

/10

1. What proportion of this square is shaded? Give your answer as a fraction.

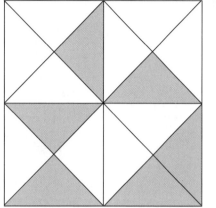

2. What proportion of this regular octagon is shaded? Give your answer as a fraction.

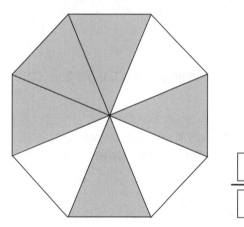

3. In a group of ten children, 4 are boys and 6 are girls.
   What is the ratio of girls to boys?

   _____

4. There is a mixture of 14 red and yellow flowers in a bunch.
   The ratio of yellow to red is 6:1. What is the total number of yellow flowers in two bunches?

   _____

5. In a box of marbles there are some black and some white.
   Jamie counted a total of 40 marbles. There are 24 black and 16 white in the box.
   What is the ratio of black to white marbles?

   _____

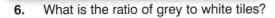

Look at the box of tiles below.

6. What is the ratio of grey to white tiles?

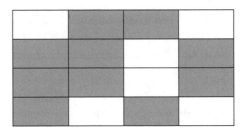

_____

7. What proportion of the tiles are white?
Give your answer as a fraction.

8. In a group of 18 children, the ratio of boys to girls is 1:1.
How many boys and girls are there in the group?

Boys = _____

Girls = _____

9. Kelly has a birthday party. The ratio of children to adults is 4:1.
There are 24 children at the party. How many adults are there?

_____

10. Look at the cups of coffee on the tray.

What is the ratio of black to white cups?

_____

/10

1. Write the value of the digit in bold in each number.

   a) 361,028 _____

   b) 19,008 _____

   c) 6,105 _____

2. Estimate the answers to the questions below and then check your answers with a calculator.

question	estimate	answer
6,138 + 8,432		
36,867 + 13,014		
4.97 + 18.01		
8,211 − 7,501		

3. Work out the value of *y* in the following equation.

   157 − *y* = 88   _____

4. Calculate $\frac{4}{9}$ of £63.

   £ _____

5. Here are the weights of some children. Work out how much they weigh altogether.

   31.6kg   27.38kg   29.18kg   31.07kg   36.66kg   27.5kg

   _____kg

6. Add these numbers.

    a)   516 + 157   _____

    b)   347 + 611   _____

    c)   610 + 705   _____

7. Richard went shopping and spent £12.60 on food, £5.50 on some socks and £10 on a scarf. How much money did he have left out of £30?

    £ _____

8. A pantomime has 38 rows of seats. There are 62 seats in each row.
How many people can have seats during the pantomime?

_____

9. Calculate the answers to these divisions.

    a)   72 ÷ 6 =   _____   **b)**   48 ÷ 8 = _____

    c)   160 ÷ 5 =   _____   **d)**   19 ÷ 6 = _____

10. Andy puts £500 in a bank account. The money earns 8% interest per year.
How much money does Andy have in the account after 1 year's interest is added?

    £ _____

/10

1. Order these decimals, starting with the **smallest**.

   a)   3.2   3.11   3.67   3.09   3.049

   b)   80.7   80.81   84.38   80.06   84.5

   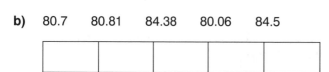

2. Estimate how much water is in this jug.

   _____ ml

3. $3b = 4a - c + 16$

   Find the value of b when $a = 7$ and $c = 2$.

   _____

4. Calculate $\frac{5}{8}$ of £96.

   £ _____

5. Convert the following quantities into decimal form.

   a)   7180g   _____ kg

   b)   254g   _____ kg

   c)   5888ml   _____ l

   d)   3469cm   _____ m

6. Amy goes to the cinema and spends £5.40 to watch the film. She also buys sweets which cost £1.85 a bag. How much does Amy spend altogether?

   £ _____

Answer booklet Maths 10 Minute tests

Test 1
1. 10,835
2. **a)** two hundred **b)** two thousand **c)** twenty thousand
3. **a)** 1,553 **b)** 4,224 **c)** 3,530
4. **a)** 1,067, 2,799, 2,809, 2,851, 4,001 **b)** 6,001, 6,099, 6,430, 6,515, 7,000
5. **a)** 11,111, 10,380, 10,307, 10,019, 9,984 **b)** 49,984, 40,621, 40,440, 40,019, 5,987
6. **a)** 4.03, 4.09, 4.099, 4.2, 4.27 **b)** 20.01, 20.72, 20.9, 24.27, 24.4
7. $\frac{1}{2}, \frac{3}{8}, \frac{1}{4}, \frac{1}{8}, \frac{1}{10}$
8. **a)** Billy **b)** Eric **c)** Jon
9. **a)** B **b)** A **c)** D
10. **a)** United **b)** City

Test 2
1. **a)** 440, 370, 900, 250, 670 **b)** 6,480, 7,050, 8,890, 5,810, 1,560 **c)** 29,840, 18,000, 21,000, 99,510, 56,220
2. **a)** 200, 1,000, 700, 300, 500 **b)** 5,800, 4,200, 6,700, 3,400, 7,600 **c)** 23,100, 57,900, 31,000, 90,000, 46,500 **d)** 128,300, 451,200, 927,000, 370,000, 701,000
3. **a)** 1000, 3,000, 6,000, 8,000, 4,000 **b)** 12,000, 30,000, 68,000, 37,000, 100,000 **c)** 222,000, 709,000, 502,000, 199,000, 450,000
4. Child 1 = 1.2m, Child 2 = 1.3m, Child 3 = 1.2m Child 4 = 1.4m, Child 5 = 1.3m, Child 6 = 1.5m
5.

Question	Estimate (between these numbers)	Answer
2,129 + 3,454	5,300 to 5,700	5,583
24,783 + 15,031	39,000 to 40,000	39,814
7.92 + 15.01	22 to 23	22.93
5,203 – 3,487	1,500 to 2,000	1,716

6. Answers between 2,100ml and 2,400ml (exact =2,250ml)
7. Answers between 12kg and 14kg
8. Answers between 1.78m and 1.93m
9. Answers between 60 minutes and 62.5 minutes
10. Answers between 2,500 weeks and 2,600 weeks

Test 3
1.

3	6	12	24	48	96

2.

160	80	40	20	10	5

3. □ ○ △ □ ○ △ □

4.

–14	–8	–2	4	10	16

5.

13	5	–3	–11	–19	–27

6. 8°C
7. 8°C
8. –5°C
9. 6°C
10. 24 hours

Test 4
1. 67
2. 216
3. 40
4. Blue marbles = 75 Yellow marbles = 25
5. Adults = 50   Children = 150
6. 27
7. Shortest = 9cm   Longest = 18cm
8. 4 years
9. 18
10. 42

Test 5
1.

Proper Fraction	Improper Fraction	Mixed Number Fraction
$\frac{1}{2}$	$\frac{11}{8}$	$6\frac{1}{3}$
$\frac{8}{10}$	$\frac{6}{4}$	$3\frac{7}{12}$

2. $a = \frac{2}{8}$ or $\frac{1}{4}$ $b = \frac{5}{16}$ $c = \frac{6}{26}$ or $\frac{3}{13}$ $d = \frac{2}{6}$ or $\frac{1}{3}$
3. $\frac{3}{4}$ or $\frac{75}{100}$, 2 and $\frac{4}{10}$ or 2 and $\frac{2}{5}$, $\frac{1}{100}$, 8 and $\frac{1}{4}$, $\frac{17}{100}$, $\frac{7}{8}$
4. $\frac{1}{3}, \frac{2}{5}, \frac{7}{15}$, $\frac{1}{2}, \frac{8}{10}, \frac{6}{4}$
5. £24
6. 3.3 l
7. £13.30
8. 69
9. 858kg
10. 1600ml

Test 6
1. 8.2
2. **a)** five hundredths **b)** five tenths **c)** five thousandths
3. **a)** 0.6 **b)** 2.8 **c)** 7.64 **d)** 0.18
4. **a)** 3.6 **b)** 20.4 **c)** 42.7 **d)** 26.04
5. **a)** 1.6 **b)** 11.2 **c)** 13.89 **d)** 37.83
6.

	Old Amount	New Amount
Carrots	1200g	2.4kg
Potatoes	2.5kg	5kg
Tomatoes	0.45kg	0.9kg
Onions	3	6
Peas	300g	0.6kg

7. £71.56
8. 163.63kg
9. 220l
10. 170m

Test 7
1. **a)** 71 **b)** 109 **c)** 143
2. **a)** 436 **b)** 729 **c)** 1235
3. **a)** 106 **b)** 122 **c)** 101
4. **a)** 595 **b)** 1132 **c)** 1360
5. 3050
6. £7.35
7. £79.39
8. 155m
9. £17.02
10. 829 + 164 = 993

Test 8
1. **a)** 46 **b)** 58 **c)** 33
2. **a)** 213 **b)** 239 **c)** 146
3. **a)** 48 **b)** 16 **c)** 42
4. **a)** 564 **b)** 176 **c)** 467
5. 797,788
6. £7.73
7. £3.60
8. 3.3kg
9. 8 mins
10. 944 – 398   = 546

Test 9
1. **a)** 12 **b)** 63 **c)** 40
2. 18, 66, 96
3. 27, 180
4. **a)** 84 **b)** 60 **c)** 90 **d)** 162
5. 888
6. 782
7. £348
8. 1,512
9. 840
10. £312.25

Test 10
1. **a)** 1, 2, 3, 4, 6, 8, 12, 24 **b)** 1, 5, 7, 35 **c)** 1, 2, 3, 6, 7, 14, 21, 42
2. 80, 24, 64
3. 72, 30, 18
4. **a)** 21 **b)** 8 **c)** 24 **d)** 3 r1
5. 35 r3
6. 74 r5
7. 24 sweets each   1 sweet left over
8. 59
9. 66
10. 28

Test 11
1. **a)** 50% **b)** 25% **c)** 30% **d)** 75%
2. **a)** 34% **b)** 57% **c)** 70% **d)** 3%
3. **a)** 0.49 **b)** 0.72 **c)** 0.05 **d)** 0.6
4. **a)** 10% **b)** 32% **c)** 23% **d)** 65%
5. **a)** 21kg **b)** 32l **c)** 1.5km **d)** £35
6. **a)** £36 **b)** 60m **c)** £1.20 **d)** 180kg
7. £2
8. £321
9. 82.8kg
10. 1000km

Test 12
1. $\frac{6}{16}$ or $\frac{3}{8}$
2. $\frac{5}{8}$
3. 6:4 or 3:2
4. 24
5. 24:16 or 12:8 or 6:4 or 3:2
6. 10:6 or 5:3
7. $\frac{6}{16}$ or $\frac{3}{8}$
8. Boys = 9, Girls = 9
9. 6
10. 7:5

Test 13
1. a) One thousand b) Ten thousand
   c) One hundred
2.

Question	Estimate	Answer
6,138 + 8,432	14,500	14,570
36,867 + 13,014	50,000	49,881
4.97 + 18.01	23	22.98
8,211 − 7,501	700	710

3. 69
4. £28
5. 183.39kg
6. a) 673 b) 958 c) 1315
7. £1.90
8. 2,356
9. a) 12 b) 6 c) 32 d) 3 r1
10. £540

Test 14
1. a) 3.049 3.09 3.11 3.2 3.67
   b) 80.06 80.7 80.81 84.38 84.5
2. 650ml to 750ml
3. 14
4. £60
5. a) 7.18kg b) 0.254kg c) 5.888l
   d) 34.69m
6. £7.25
7. 261,039
8. 1,148
9. 20, 105, 55
10. 180m

Test 15
1.

Test 16
1.

```
D  I M P R O P E R F R A C T I O N
D E  F  R R    T N I O P     E
I  G  A  I E Q U A L     D   T
V  R C  G G    G     I   G U
I  E  I E  M U S     O     E N
S K  E N T T  M   B   H N O I
I  I  D V  N A  E   U   P O M M
O  T G E  I L  D C  D   A G E
N E  N   L   I   R   R Y T
L      Y   A   I   G L R
K I L O M E T R E  N   H   R O Y
T        R T   A P
R C  R A T I O  A   B
R E O   N   C L O C K W I S E
E  M S O  E U   I   L
T  P G  N  G O D   C
R  A H A  G  E R T   R
A E E N  S T I N U R  E H  I
U R O  H S   Z   C
Q E A N E G A T I V E  H E I G H T
```

Test 17
1. A three sided polygon is a *triangle*.
   An eight sided polygon is an *octagon*.
   A five sided polygon is a *pentagon*.
   A seven sided polygon is a *heptagon*.
   A ten sided polygon is a *decagon*.
2. 15cm
3.

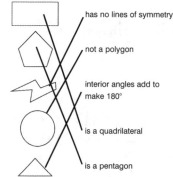

4. Any four sided shape with at least one side a different length.
5.

6.

7.

8. 12
9. 50cm
10. 105°

Test 18
1. a) 6 b) 3 c) 1
2. a) 12 b) 1 c) 8
3. a) 0 b) 8 c) 4
4. B and C
5. 343cm³
6. 314cm²
7. 150m³
8. 100cm²
9. 216cm³
10. B and D

Test 19
1.

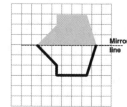

2.

3.

4. H and B
5. C
6.
7.
8.

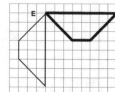

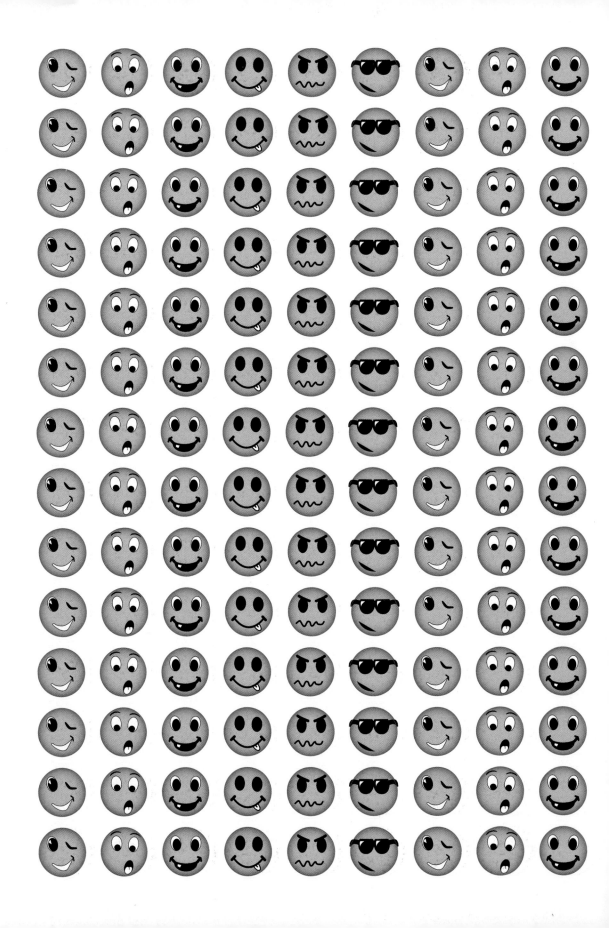

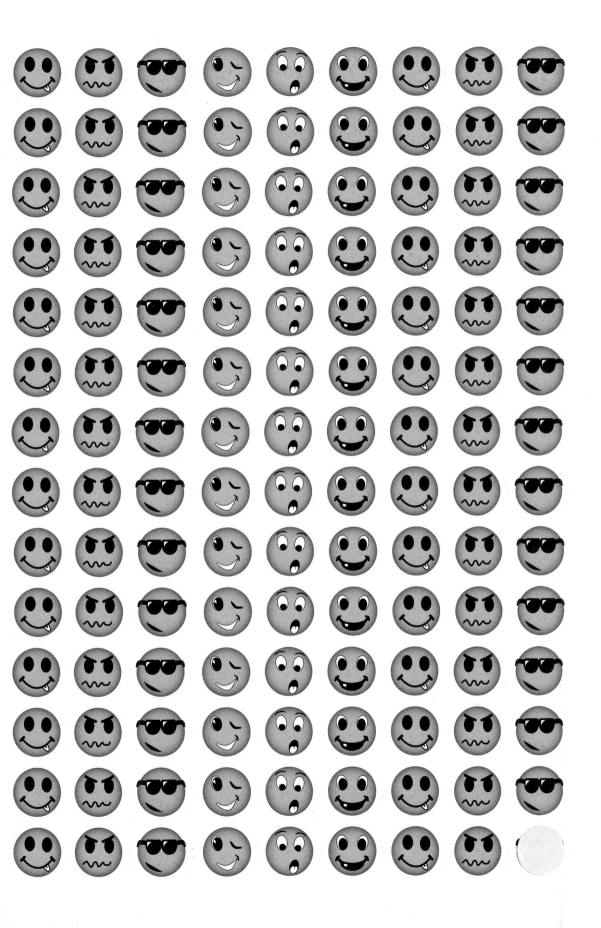

9.

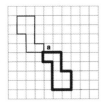

10.

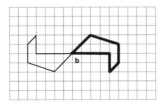

Test 20
1. A = (1, 4) B = (3, 6) C = (3, 0)
   D = (5, 1)
2. A = (1, 0) B = (2, 6) C = (7, 8)
   D = (9, 4)

3.

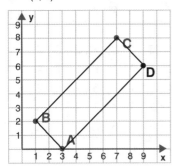

4. P = (0.2, 0.6) Q = (0.6, 0.9)
   R = (0.7, 0.5) S = (0.5, 0.1)
5. B = (0, 13) C = (2, 1) D = (3, 11)
   E = (10, 6)

6.

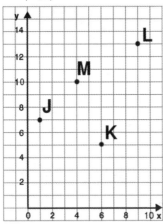

7. **a)** Park (18, 12) **b)** Market (4, 14)
   c) Pool (17, 1)
8. M = (−1, 1) N = (1, 4) O = (−3, −2)
   P = (2, −5)

9.

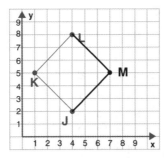

10.

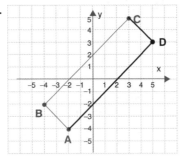

Test 21

1.

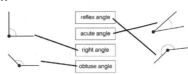

2. Answers in between the following X
   = 20° to 30° and Y = 65° to 75°
3. Answers in between the following a
   = 130° to 140° and b = 95° to 105°
4. 110°
5. 70°
6. 130° (126° to 134° is acceptable)
7. 40° (36° to 44° is acceptable)
8. Answers ± 3°

a = 50°	b = 100°	c = 30°

9. 235° Answers ± 4°
10. Answers ± 4°

s = 140°	t = 320°

Test 22
1. **a)** 300cm **b)** 4.5cm **c)** 3,500m
   d) 12.35m
2. **a)** 3.5kg **b)** 0.75tonnes **c)** 4,060g
   d) 4,200kg
3. **a)** 35ml **b)** 3.45l **c)** 9,052ml **d)** 4.57cl
4. 8.75kg or 8kg 750g
5. 2.2l or 2l and 200ml
6. **a)** 7.6cm or 76mm **b)** 4.2cm or
   42mm **c)** 5.5cm or 55mm
7. 1100g or 1.1kg or 1kg 100g
8. 15,000ml
9. 14km
10. **a)** 15°C **b)** 17°C **c)** -13°C

Test 23
1. $\frac{1}{6}$
2. 2,700 secs
3. 255 mins
4. 1,440 mins
5. **a)** 8th September 2010
   b) 27th August
6. **a)** 55 minutes
   b) 20:20
7. Thursday
8. 80 minutes or 1 hour and 20 minutes
9. 29 mins and 45 secs
10. 140 mins

Test 24
1. 40cm
2. 11cm²
3. 6.4cm
4. 5,512m²
5. 30cm
6. Square must be 5 x 5 e.g.

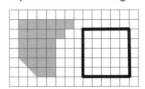

7.

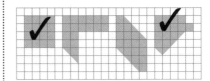

8.

9. Area = 25cm² Perimeter = 28cm
10. 119cm²

Test 25
1. dark grey
2. white and pale grey
3. 2
4. pale grey
5. pale grey
6. B
7. B
8. C
9. C and D
10. B and D

Test 26
1. £2000
2. £900
3. 1.8m
4. 0.5m
5. 68mm (accept 67 to 69)
6. 23mm (accept 21 to 25)
7. It did not rain on those days.
8. 18 days

9. 75

10. 50 (accept 45 to 55)

Test 27

1. 26 (accept 24 to 28)

2. 28 (accept 26 to 30)

3. £6

4. £41 (accept 40 to 42)

5. 45 (accept 42 to 48)

6. 10 (accept 7 to 13)

7. 13 (accept 10 to 15)

8. 20:00 or 8pm

9. 26°C (accept 25°C to 27°C)

10. 13:00 or 1pm (accept 12:30 to 13:30)

Test 28

1. 12

2. Jake

3. 8.4

4. 21

5. 22

6. Mode = 15   Mean = 13   Median = 13

7. pale grey

8. £11.80

9. White

10. Mode = 4 Mean = 5 Median = 4

Test 29

9	8	6	5	2	7	4	3	1
3	5	7	9	1	4	8	6	2
1	2	4	6	3	8	9	7	5
7	6	8	2	4	1	5	9	3
2	1	9	3	5	6	7	8	4
4	3	5	8	7	9	2	1	6
6	9	3	4	8	2	1	5	7
8	7	2	1	6	5	3	4	9
5	4	1	7	9	3	6	2	8

Test 30

5	6	2	7	8	4	9	3	1
1	3	8	6	2	9	5	7	4
4	7	9	5	3	1	6	8	2
6	8	5	1	4	3	7	2	9
2	1	4	9	6	7	3	5	8
7	9	3	8	5	2	1	4	6
9	2	1	3	7	8	4	6	5
8	5	7	4	9	6	2	1	3
3	4	6	2	1	5	8	9	7

Test 31

9	5	6	1	4	8	7	3	2
7	4	3	2	9	5	8	6	1
1	8	2	3	6	7	4	5	9
4	2	9	5	7	6	1	8	3
8	6	7	4	1	3	2	9	5
3	1	5	9	8	2	6	7	4
6	9	1	7	5	4	3	2	8
2	7	4	8	3	9	5	1	6
5	3	8	6	2	1	9	4	7

Test 32

3	4	5	6	8	7	2	1	9
2	8	6	9	1	5	4	7	3
7	1	9	2	4	3	5	8	6
8	7	2	5	9	4	3	6	1
1	6	4	3	7	2	8	9	5
9	5	3	1	6	8	7	4	2
4	3	1	7	5	9	6	2	8
6	2	8	4	3	1	9	5	7
5	9	7	8	2	6	1	3	4

Test 33

21 squares

7. Take away 844,273 from 1,105,312.

_____

8. A box has 28 books in it. There are 41 boxes in the store room.
How many books are there altogether?

_____

9. Circle all the numbers which have a factor of 5.

52   20   14   105   55

10. A rope is 120m long. The length is increased by 50% when another rope is tied to it.
How long is the rope now?

_____ m

/10

Crossword fun

Try this maths crossword, using the clues below.

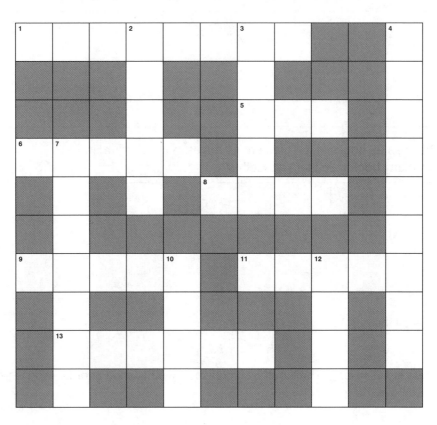

Across

1. Any three sided polygon. (8)

5. The product of 5 and 2. (3)

6. $104 - 8^2$ (5)

8. Nothing at all. (4)

9. A square based pyramid has 5 of these. (5)

11. Add all the numbers in a sum together to get this. (5)

13. The point of intersection of the x and y axis. (6)

Down

2. An angle of less than 90°. (5)

3. The metric version of a pint. (5)

4. Any polygon with different length sides has this property. (9)

7. Any shape with 8 sides. (7)

10. Another name for an operation in a calculation. (4)

12. The units for this could be seconds. (4)

Can you find all the maths terms in this wordsearch?

D	E	I	M	P	R	O	P	E	R	F	R	A	C	T	I	O	N	B	E
D	E	G	A	F	S	R	R	Y	L	F	S	T	N	I	O	P	S	E	E
I	P	G	L	A	W	I	E	Q	U	A	L	V	B	C	F	A	D	O	T
V	L	Q	R	C	A	G	G	S	A	W	W	G	A	R	L	I	N	G	U
I	Q	F	B	E	S	I	E	Z	M	U	S	D	E	D	O	M	N	E	N
S	O	K	O	V	E	N	T	T	Q	R	M	Q	F	B	D	H	N	O	I
I	I	I	Z	D	V	C	N	A	O	R	E	P	U	A	R	P	O	M	M
O	Y	T	G	L	E	P	I	L	I	N	D	C	F	D	D	A	G	E	C
N	A	E	M	J	N	Y	I	L	C	O	I	P	A	R	O	R	Y	T	H
A	L	A	F	J	R	W	U	Y	U	I	A	T	D	I	E	G	L	R	L
K	I	L	O	M	E	T	R	E	C	X	N	R	Q	H	E	R	O	Y	W
C	T	A	C	T	Y	N	C	K	K	V	O	R	H	T	N	A	P	P	O
E	R	C	O	O	R	A	T	I	O	N	A	A	F	J	S	B	N	F	J
R	E	W	O	D	F	T	S	S	N	I	C	L	O	C	K	W	I	S	E
E	A	F	J	M	B	S	P	O	D	U	E	U	F	S	O	I	A	V	L
T	Z	X	V	I	P	P	G	S	T	N	Q	G	A	O	R	D	D	Z	C
R	L	A	A	H	L	A	I	A	G	P	U	E	S	R	A	T	I	A	R
A	P	E	E	I	N	W	S	T	I	N	U	R	D	E	Z	H	N	L	I
U	A	R	Y	O	D	R	H	S	F	F	S	D	W	Z	T	S	P	W	C
Q	E	A	N	E	G	A	T	I	V	E	T	A	I	H	E	I	G	H	T

Area	Geometry	Origin
Bar graph	Height	Polygon
Compass	Improper Fraction	Point
Circle	Integer	Quarter
Clockwise	Kilometre	Ratio
Cuboid	Kite	Regular
Division	Litre	Sphere
Degree	Length	Sum
Edge	Median	Tally
Equal	Minute	Third
Even	Negative	Unit
Face	Nonagon	Width

1. Fill in the gaps to make the following sentences correct.

   A three sided polygon is a _____ .

   An eight sided polygon is an _____ .

   A five sided polygon is a _____ .

   A seven sided polygon is a _____ .

   A ten sided polygon is a _____ .

2. An equilateral triangle has a perimeter of 45cm. What is the length of each side?

   _____ cm

3. Look at the following shapes and match to the correct description.

      has no lines of symmetry

      not a polygon

      interior angles add to make 180°

      is a quadrilateral

      is a pentagon

4. In the grid below, complete the drawing to make an irregular quadrilateral.

   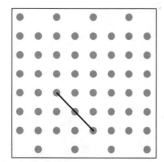

5. Draw all the diagonals on the pentagon below.

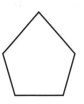

6. Put a tick in the shapes which have any parallel sides.

    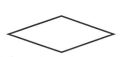

7. Here are 5 shapes, tick the two which have lines of symmetry.

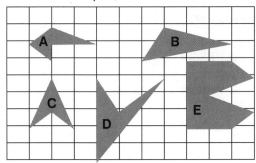

8. How many squares with a perimeter of 26cm each will fit into the rectangle below?

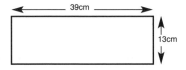

_____

9. Look at the kite below, what is the perimeter of the shape?

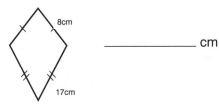   _____ cm

10. Angle c = 90º and Angle b = 60º, so what is Angle a?

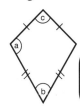   a = _____°

/10

1. How many **faces** do the following 3D shapes have?

    a) Cube _____ faces

    b) Cylinder _____ faces

    c) Sphere _____ faces

2. How many **edges** do the following 3D shapes have?

    a) Cuboid _____ edges

    b) Cone _____ edges

    c) Square-based pyramid _____ edges

3. How many **vertices** do the following 3D shapes have?

    a) Cylinder _____ vertices

    b) Cube _____ vertices

    c) Triangular based pyramid _____ vertices

4. Which two of the following are correct nets for a cuboid?

    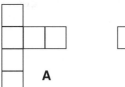 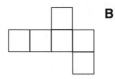 **B**

    A

    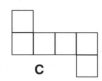   _____ and _____

    C   D

5. What is the volume of a cube with an edge that measures 7cm?

    _____ cm^3

6. What is the surface area of this cuboid?

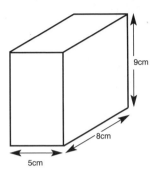

_____ cm²

9cm

8cm

5cm

7. What is the volume of this open top tank?

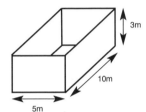

_____ m³

3m

10m

5m

8. A cube has a volume of 1000cm³. What is the area of each face?

_____ cm²

9. What is the volume of the cube which has this net?

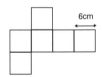

6cm

_____ cm³

10. Which of the following are correct nets for a cuboid? _____

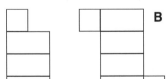

B

D

A

C

/10

1. Using a ruler, complete the diagram below to make a symmetrical shape.

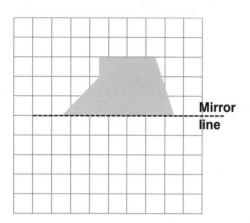
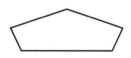

Mirror line

2. Using a ruler, draw the reflection of this shape.

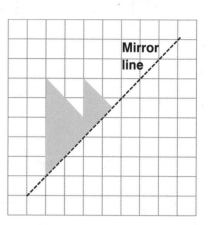

Mirror line

3. Look at the shapes below and put a tick inside the shapes with at least one line of symmetry.

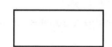

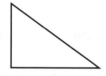

4. Which of these letters are symmetrical?

F   H   B   J   _____ and _____

5. Look at the shape in the diagram below. Write the letter of the shape that would be its reflection.

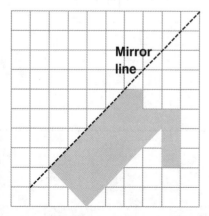

Mirror line

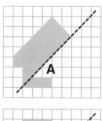

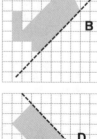

Letter

_____

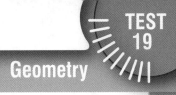

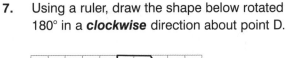

6. Using a ruler, draw the shape below rotated 90° in a *clockwise* direction about point B.

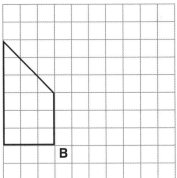

7. Using a ruler, draw the shape below rotated 180° in a *clockwise* direction about point D.

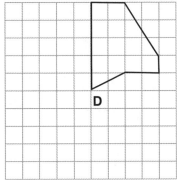

8. Using a ruler, draw the shape below rotated 90° in an *anti-clockwise* direction about point E.

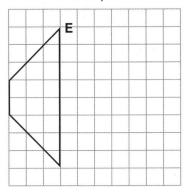

9. Using a ruler, draw the shape below rotated 180° in an *anti-clockwise* direction about point a.

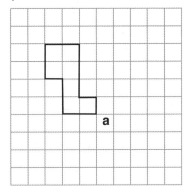

10. Using a ruler, draw the shape below rotated 180° in an *anti-clockwise* direction about point b.

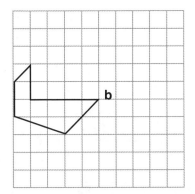

/10

Coordinates

1. Write down the coordinates A, B, C & D.

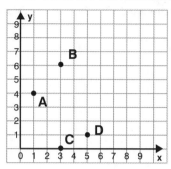

A = (,   )   B = (,   )
C = (,   )   D = (,   )

2. Write down the coordinates A, B, C & D.

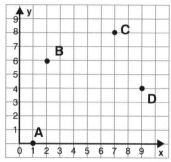

A = (,   )   B = (,   )
C = (,   )   D = (,   )

3. Points A, B, C and D make a rectangle. Plot the missing point D on the grid and complete the rectangle.

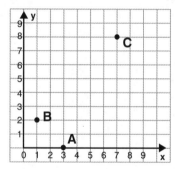

4. Write down the coordinates P, Q, R & S.
P = (,   )   Q = (,   )
R = (,   )   S = (,   )

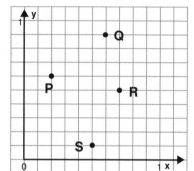

5. Write down the coordinates B, C, D & E.
B = (,   )   C = (,   )
D = (,   )   E = (,   )

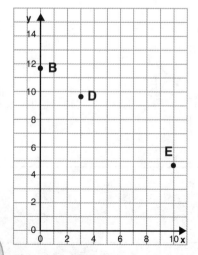

6. Plot these coordinates on the grid below.
J (1 , 7)   K (6 , 5)
L (9 , 13)   M (4 , 10)

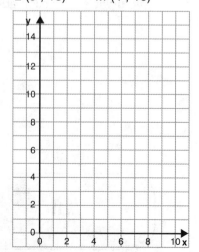

7.

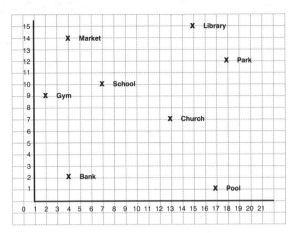

a) Where is the park?

_____

b) Where is the market?

_____

c) Where is the pool?

_____

8. Write down the coordinates M, N, O & P.

M = (,   )   N = (,   )

O = (,   )   P = (,   )

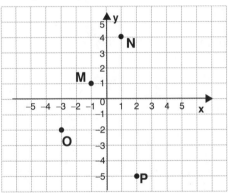

9. Plot point M on the grid below to complete the square JKLM.

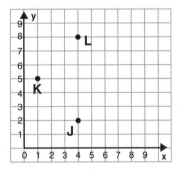

10. Plot point D on the grid below and complete the rectangle ABCD.

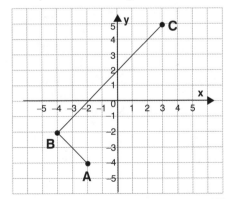

/10

1. Join the angles up to the correct labels.

reflex angle
acute angle
right angle
obtuse angle

2. Estimate the size of the acute angles below. (Do not use a protractor).

x = _____

y = _____

3. Estimate the size of the obtuse angles below. (Do not use a protractor).

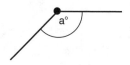

a = _____

b = _____

4. Look at the parallelogram below and calculate the angle x. (Do not use a protractor).

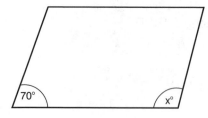

x = _____

70°   x°

5. Calculate the angle on the isosceles triangle below.
(Do not use a protractor).

x = _____

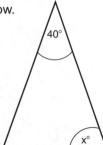

40°

x°

6. Measure angle x accurately. Use a protractor.

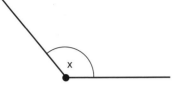

x = _____

7. Measure angle z accurately. Use a protractor.

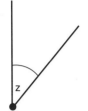

z = _____

8. Measure all the angles in this triangle. Use a protractor.

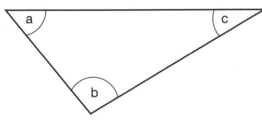

a = _____ °

b = _____ °

c = _____ °

9. Measure angle y accurately. Use a protractor.

y = _____

10. Measure accurately the two angles below. Use a protractor.

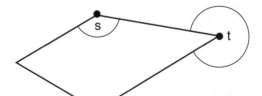

s = _____ °

t = _____ °

/10

1. Convert these units of length.

   a) 3m = _____ cm

   b) 45mm = _____ cm

   c) 3.5km = _____ m

   d) 1235cm = _____ m

2. Convert these units of weight.

   a) 3500g = _____ kg

   b) 750kg = _____ tonnes

   c) 4.06kg = _____ g

   d) 4.2tonnes = _____ kg

3. Convert these units of capacity.

   a) 3.5cl = _____ ml

   b) 3450ml = _____ l

   c) 9.052l = _____ ml

   d) 457ml = _____ cl

4. What is the reading on the scale below?

   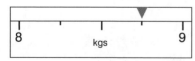

   _____ kg

5. How much water is in this jug?

   _____ litres

6. Measure the lengths of these three lines with your ruler.

a) _____ _____

b) _____ _____

c) _____ _____

7. How much more flour do you need to add to these kitchen scales to make 1.8kg?

_____ kg

8. When opened, a tap lets 100ml of water through every second.
How much water passes through the open tap in 2.5 minutes?   _____ ml

9. A man walks 1.4km to work every day and at the end of the day walks back home again.
How many kilometres does the man walk in a normal five day working week?

_____ km

10. Write down the readings on these three thermometers.

a) _____°C

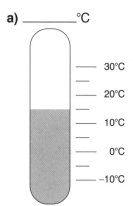

b) _____°C

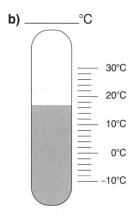

c) _____°C

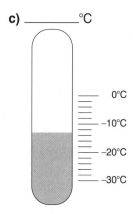

/10

1. What fraction of 3 hours is 30 minutes?

$$\frac{\boxed{}}{\boxed{}}$$

2. How many seconds are there in 45 minutes?

_____ secs

3. Jon sets out from school at 3:30pm. He then goes to see his Grandma and eventually gets home at 19:45. How many minutes after he left school did he arrive at home?

_____ mins

4. How many minutes are there in 24 hours?

_____ mins

5. Here is a calendar for September 2010.

September 2010						
Sun	Mon	Tue	Wed	Thu	Fri	Sat
			1	2	3	4
5	6	7	8	9	10	11
12	13	14	15	16	17	18
19	20	21	22	23	24	25
26	27	28	29	30		

a) School starts on the second Wednesday of the month, what date is that?

_____

b) Jack arrives back from holiday on the last Friday in August, what date is that?

_____

6. a) Billy gets to the cinema at 17:30. The film starts at 18:25, how long must Billy wait before the film starts?

_____

b) The film lasts for 115 minutes. What time does it finish?

_____

7. Here is a calendar for July 2010.

July 2010						
Sun	Mon	Tue	Wed	Thu	Fri	Sat
				1	2	3
4	5	6	7	8	9	10
11	12	13	14	15	16	17
18	19	20	21	22	23	24
25	26	27	28	29	30	31

Sally goes on holiday for 10 days, and she arrives back on the 4th of July.
What day of the week did Sally leave on?

_____

8. What is $\frac{2}{3}$ of 2 hours? _____

9. Sasha can run a kilometre in 4 minutes and 15 seconds.
If Sasha runs at the same speed, how long will it take her to run 7 kilometres?

_____

10. James puts on a DVD to watch at twenty five past five. The DVD finishes at quarter to eight.
How many minutes does the DVD last for?

_____ mins

/10

1. What is the perimeter of the shape below?

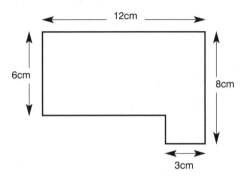

_____ cm

2. Look at this shape on the cm square grid.

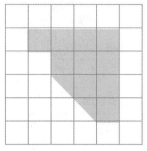

What is the area of this shape?

_____ cm²

3. A regular pentagon has a perimeter of 32cm.

What is the length of each side of the pentagon? _____ cm

4. What is the area of this football pitch? _____ m²

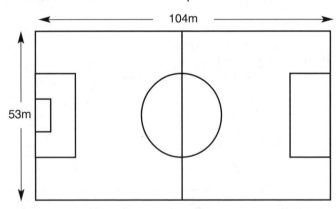

5. Look at this shape on the cm square grid.

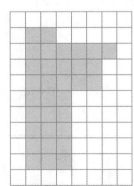

What is the perimeter of this shape?

_____ cm

6. On the grid below, draw a square with the same area as the shaded shape.

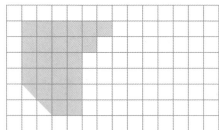

7. Tick the two shapes below which have the same area.

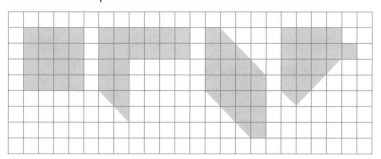

8. Tick the two shapes below which have the same perimeter.

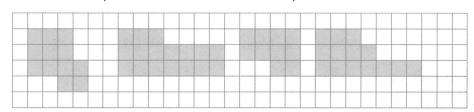

9. Work out the area and perimeter of the shape on the cm grid below.

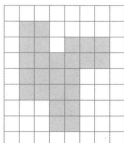

Area = _____

Perimeter = _____

10. What is the area of the isosceles triangle below? _____ cm²

17cm

14cm

/10

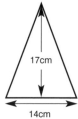

1. What colour ball is the most likely to be drawn out of the bag below?

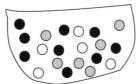

_____

2. Which colour balls are equally likely to be drawn from the bag below?

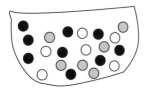

_____ and _____

3. Look at the spinner below. Which number is most likely to come up?

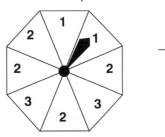

_____

4. Look at the spinner below. Which colour is most likely to come up?

_____

5. Look at the spinner below. Which colour is least likely to come up?

_____

6. Dawn has a bag of marbles. There are 7 red marbles, 4 green marbles, 6 white marbles and 3 black marbles. Dawn picks a marble from the bag at random. Which statement below is correct? Underline it.

    A   There is an even chance on picking a red marble.

    B   Dawn is twice as likely to pick a white marble than a black marble.

    C   Dawn is certain to pick a red or white marble.

    D   She has no chance of picking a black marble.

7. Pat rolls 2 six sided dice which are each numbered 1 to 6. He then adds the two numbers together. Which statement below is true?

    A   Pat will roll two sixes.

    B   He is most likely to roll 7.

    C   Pat will roll an even number.

    D   He will not roll 7.

8. Which spinner below has the most chance of coming up with a 1?

A   **B**   **C**   **D**

9. Tick the statements below which are correct.

    A   It is certain to rain today.

    B   It is likely to go dark tonight.

    C   Tomorrow is the day after today.

    D   I am certain to be older tomorrow.

10. Tick the statements below which are incorrect.

    A   It is certain to go dark tonight.

    B   Tomorrow it will snow.

    C   It is unlikely I will ever be a king or queen.

    D   The sun is likely to set today.

/10

The bar graph below shows the amount of money a shop took in one week.

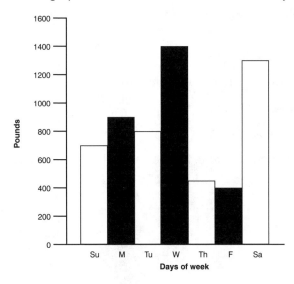

1. How much money did the shop take at the weekend?

£ _____

2. How much money did the shop take on Monday?

£ _____

The bar line graph below shows how far some children can jump.

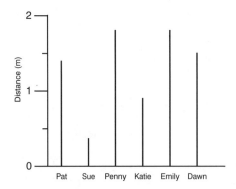

3. How far did Emily jump? _____ m

4. How much further did Pat jump than Katie? _____ m

The line graph below shows the accumulative rainfall during March in one year.

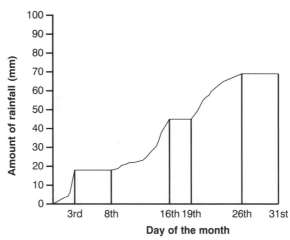

5. How much rainfall was there in the whole month? _____ mm

6. How much rainfall was there between the 16th and 31st of the month? _____ mm

7. Why does the graph flatten off in three places?

_____

8. How many days were wet during the month? _____ days

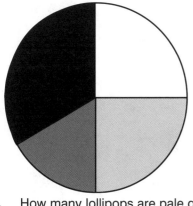

There are 300 ice lollipops in a freezer of four different colours. The amount of each colour is represented below.

9. How many lollipops are pale grey? _____

10. Approximately, how many lollipops are mid grey? _____

/10

Tables, charts and graphs 2

The number of chocolate bars sold at a school tuck shop is shown below.

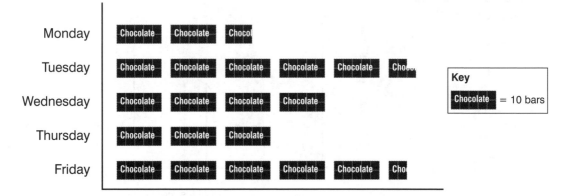

1. How many chocolate bars were sold on Monday?

   _____ bars

2. How many more chocolate bars were sold on Friday than Monday?

   _____ bars

Look at the bar chart.

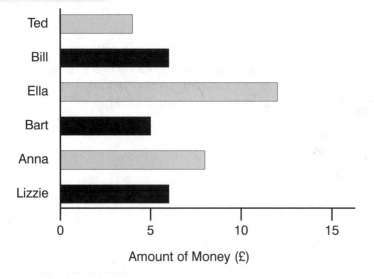

Amount of Money (£)

3. How much pocket money did Bill get?   £ _____

4. How much money did the children receive altogether?   £ _____

The Pie Chart below shows the sort of pets 100 children have.

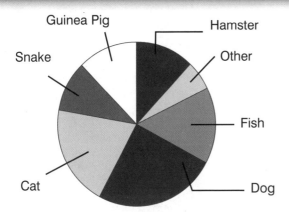

Guinea Pig   Hamster

Snake   Other

Fish

Cat   Dog

5. Approximately, how many children have a dog or a cat?   _____

6. Estimate the number of children who have a pet snake.   _____

7. Estimate how many more children have a dog than a hamster.   _____

The temperature in a conservatory was recorded every two hours and recorded on the graph.

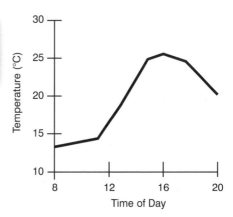

8. At what time was the last temperature reading taken?   _____

9. What was the approximate temperature at 4pm?   _____°C

10. When did the temperature first hit 20°C?   _____

/10

Averages

1. Write down the mode in this list of ten numbers.

12	14	9	14	12	12	9	15	18	4

   _____

2. Write down the modal name out of this group.

Shane	Jake
Bart	Mick
Will	Jake
Jack	Jack
Jake	Bart
Shane	Callum

   _____

3. Calculate the mean in this list of ten numbers.

8	7	7	9	4	12	10	7	11	9

   _____

4. Circle the median number in this list.

11	12	18	21	25	26	34

5. Find the median number in these 11 numbers.

24	18	19	28	30	9	43	57	16	22	1

   _____

6. Find the mode, mean and median of this set of numbers.

15	12	8	15	15	8	10	10	17	13	20

Mode =
Mean =
Median =

7. Look at the box of tiles below.

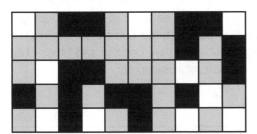

What is the modal colour of the tiles?

_____

8. A group of children do a sponsored walk. Here is the amount of money each child raised.

Name	Amount (£)
Jess	10.20
Kate	12.90
Paul	8.50
Wendy	14.00
Raul	13.40

What is the mean amount of money raised by each child?

£ _____

9. Nine athletes ran in a 100m race. Here are their finishing times:

Lane	Name	Time (secs)
1	White	10.00
2	Green	9.82
3	Smith	10.07
4	Brown	10.30
5	Jones	9.84
6	Black	10.22
7	Day	9.90
8	Edwards	10.12
9	Cork	9.91

Which athlete ran the median time?_____

10. Find the mode, mean and median of this set of numbers.

3	8	4	3	2	4	7	6	9	5	4

Mode =
Mean =
Median =

/10

Sudoku

Each of these puzzles will take about 10 minutes!

Sudoku is a logic puzzle. It is presented as a square grid with 9 squares to a side. Thick grid lines emphasize each block of 9 squares. The grid is partially filled with the numbers 1 through to 9. To solve the puzzle, the empty squares are filled in so that each row, column and block contains each of the numbers 1 through to 9. There is only one correct answer.

29.

	8			2	7		3	1
		7	9	1	4		6	
1			3	8				5
7	6	8	2	4	1		9	3
			3	5	6	7		
4	3	5	8		9	2	1	6
6		3	4		2	1		
	7	2	1		5		4	
5								

30.

5						9	3	
1				2			7	
	7	9		3	1	6	8	2
6	8	5	1			7	2	
			9		7			
	9	3			2	1	4	6
9	2	1	3	7		4	6	
	5			9				3
	4	6						7

31.

9			1	4	8		3	
			2			6	1	
	8	2	3	6				
4	2		5	7				3
8								5
3			8	2		7	4	
			5	4	3	2		
2	7			9				
	3		6	2	1			7

32.

			8	7		1		
2		6				4	7	
			2	4			8	6
8		2		9		3		
	6	4	3		2	8	9	
		3		6		7		2
4	3			5	9			
	2	8				9		7
	9		8	2	6			

How many squares can you find on the picture below? Look carefully, there are more than you think!

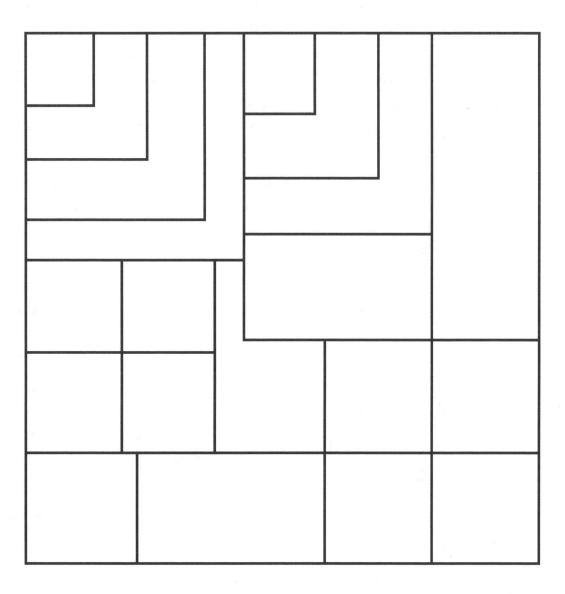

_____ squares

Progress report

Test 1	Test 2	Test 3	Test 4	Test 5
Level 4	**Level 4**	**Level 4**	**Level 4**	**Level 4**
/10	/10	/10	/10	/10
Date _____	Date _____	Date _____	Date _____	Date _____

Test 6	Test 7	Test 8	Test 9	Test 10
Level 4	**Level 4**	**Level 4**	**Level 4**	**Level 4**
/10	/10	/10	/10	/10
Date _____	Date _____	Date _____	Date _____	Date _____

Test 11	Test 12	Test 13	Test 14	Test 15
Level 4	**Level 4**	**Level 4**	**Level 4**	**If you got all of the clues in less than 10 minutes, colour this in red, or colour this in blue if it took you longer.**
/10	/10	/10	/10	
Date _____	Date _____	Date _____	Date _____	Date _____

Test 16	Test 17	Test 18	Test 19	Test 20
Did you find all of the words? If you did it in less than 10 minutes, colour this in red, or if you did it in more, colour this in blue.	**Level 4**	**Level 4**	**Level 4**	**Level 4**
	/10	/10	/10	/10
Date _____	Date _____	Date _____	Date _____	Date _____

Test 21	Test 22	Test 23	Test 24	Test 25
Level 4	**Level 4**	**Level 4**	**Level 4**	**Level 4**
/10	/10	/10	/10	/10
Date _____	Date _____	Date _____	Date _____	Date _____

Test 26	Test 27	Test 28	Test 29	Test 30
Level 4	**Level 4**	**Level 4**	**If you complete the puzzle, then colour this in red.**	**If you complete the puzzle, then colour this in red.**
/10	/10	/10		
Date _____	Date _____	Date _____	Date _____	Date _____

Test 31	Test 32	Test 33
If you complete the puzzle, then colour this in red.	**If you complete the puzzle, then colour this in red.**	**If you found the right number of squares, then colour this box in in red.**
Date _____	Date _____	Date _____

Colour each box in the correct colour to show how many questions you got right.

0–2 = yellow, 3–5 = green, 6–7 = blue, 8–10 = red

This will help you to monitor your progress.